MAGIC TREE HOUSE®
DINOSAURS BEFORE DARK

MARY POPE OSBORNE'S

MAGIC TREE HOUSE®

DINOSAURS BEFORE DARK

THE GRAPHIC NOVEL

ADAPTED BY

JENNY LAIRD

WITH ART BY

KELLY & NICHOLE MATTHEWS

SCHOLASTIC INC.

Adapted from *Dinosaurs Before Dark*, published by Random House Children's Books,
a division of Penguin Random House LLC, New York, in 1992.

ISBN 978-1-338-79605-6

12 11 10 9 8 7 6 5 4 3   22 23 24 25 26

Printed in the U.S.A.   40

First Scholastic printing, September 2021

Text adapted by Jenny Laird
The artists used Clip Studio Paint to create the illustrations for this book.
The text of this book is set in 13-point Cartoonist Hand Regular.

For Mallory and Jenna,
two of Jack and Annie's best friends
—M.P.O.

For Quinn, who was born to fly
—J.L.

We dedicate this book to our mother,
a teacher, who taught us to love reading, drawing,
and learning; our brothers, for inspiring us to follow
in their footsteps; and our cats, for never letting
us forget what is truly important (feeding them).
—K.M. & N.M.

CHAPTER ONE
Into the Woods

FROG CREEK

4

5

CHAPTER TWO
The Wish

CHAPTER THREE

Where Is Here?

Where are we?

It's the same.

Yeah, *exactly* the same.

Except real...

and alive.

But he's real, Jack.

He's very real.

Gasp!

CHAPTER FOUR
Henry

That's the problem—she doesn't think!

What does she think she's doing?

I guess I have to do the thinking for both of us.

He's soft, Jack.

He feels like Henry.

He's no dog, Annie.

But feel how soft he is, Jack.

Don't think, Jack. Just do it.

...

We're probably the first people in the whole world to ever see a real live dinosaur.

What are you doing?

Taking notes.

I wonder how smart he is.

Very smart.

Don't count on it. His brain is probably no bigger than a bean.

No, he's *very* smart.

I can feel it.

CHAPTER FIVE
Gold in the Grass

Just plants. No meat.

Let's go see him.

What?

Did you miss the part where the book said he weighs 12,000 pounds?

Don't you want to take notes about him?

Hmmm.

We're probably the first people in the whole world to ever see a real live Triceratops.

I already said that.

Let's go.

Shhhhh.

But we can't see—

Wow. He's bigger than a truck.

No, Annie.

CHAPTER SIX
Dinosaur Valley

Keep going.

...

GRRUUUAHHH!

Hmm, where are the other mothers?

ANATOSAURUS

"The Anatosauruses lived in colonies.

While a few mothers babysat the nests, others looked for food."

CHAPTER SEVEN
Ready, Set, Go!

Run, Annie! **Run!** To the tree house!

But what about the babies?

NOD

CHAPTER EIGHT
A Giant Shadow

"Tyrannosaurus rex was one of the largest meat-eating land animals of all time. If it were alive today, it could eat a human in one bite."

Great.

That's no help at all.

"Based on the structure of its ear, scientists believe the T. rex had excellent hearing."

CHAPTER NINE
The Amazing Ride

I think if we point to a picture in any of these books and make a wish to go there, the tree house will take us there.

Want to make the wish this time?

Let's do it together.

We wish we could go there!

The tree house started to spin.

It spun faster and faster.

Then everything was still.

Absolutely still.

CHAPTER TEN
Home Before Dark

Thanks for the adventure.

We'll be back.

LET THE
MAGIC TREE HOUSE®
WHISK YOU AWAY!

Read all the novels in the
#1 bestselling chapter book
series of all time!

MARY POPE OSBORNE is the author of many novels, picture books, story collections, and nonfiction books. Her #1 *New York Times* bestselling Magic Tree House® series has been translated into numerous languages around the world. Highly recommended by parents and educators everywhere, the series introduces young readers to different cultures and times, as well as to the world's legacy of ancient myth and storytelling.

JENNY LAIRD is an award-winning playwright. She collaborates with Will Osborne and Randy Courts on creating musical theater adaptations of the Magic Tree House® series for both national and international audiences. Their work also includes shows for young performers, available through Music Theatre International's Broadway Junior® Collection. Currently the team is working on a Magic Tree House® animated television series.

KELLY & NICHOLE MATTHEWS are twin sisters and a comic-art team. They get to do their dream job every day, drawing comics for a living. They've worked with Boom Studios!, Archaia, the Jim Henson Company, Hiveworks, and now Random House!